True Love Waits

A Student's Guide to the Five Love Languages

A LifeWay Ministry

Gary Chapman and Tony Rankin

LifeWay Press
Nashville, Tennessee

Published by LifeWay Press

ISBN: 0-6330-9666-0

This book is a resource in the "Personal Life"
category of the Christian Growth Study Plan.
Course CG-0994

Dewey Decimal Classification Number: 152.4
Subject Heading: LOVE

Printed in the United States of America

Student Ministry Publishing
LifeWay Church Resources
One LifeWay Plaza
Nashville, Tennessee 37234-0174

CONTENTS

WRITERS

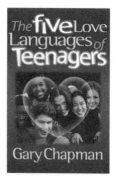

GARY CHAPMAN's best-selling book *The Five Love Languages* has helped thousands of couples develop stronger, more fulfilling relationships. Over the years, numerous parents asked Dr. Chapman to write a book that would help them understand and relate to their teenagers. His standard reply was, "Wait until I get through raising my own teenagers." That task is now completed. His daughter, Shelley, is a physician who is married and has two children of her own. His son, Derek, is a missionary in Prague who, along with his wife Amy, is seeking to reach teenagers in that European city. He and his wife, Karolyn, thoroughly enjoy their children and grandchildren.

TONY RANKIN is a clinical therapist in Nashville, Tennessee and serves as the Family Ministry Specialist for the Tennessee Baptist Convention. Most importantly he enjoys parenting with his wife, Amber. He has two teenage sons, Drew and Caleb, and a preteen daughter, Katelin. He loves to coach baseball, speak and write, and laugh at family stories. He has written more than 200 magazine articles and advice columns and has written several books. Most recently he coauthored *The Five Love Languages of Teenagers, Parent Study Guide* and wrote *When True Love Doesn't Wait*. He still enjoys reminiscing about his 13 years in youth ministry and working with the teenagers at his church.

True Love Waits Meets the Five Love Languages

I can remember sitting at the Rio Bravo® restaurant on West End in Nashville and hearing Richard Ross dream about starting the True Love Waits movement. It didn't take long to realize that his passion about teenage sexual purity would soon capture the interest of students across America and throughout the world. As a youth minister, I watched teenagers commit themselves to sexual purity. As a counselor and family specialist, I imagined the TLW movement becoming more of a family focus and envisioned parents committing themselves to a level of sexual purity not experienced in decades. True Love Waits Goes Home fulfilled that dream.

As Gary Chapman and I completed *The Five Love Languages of Teenagers*, a video series and workbook for your parents, I was thrilled to hear that a book would be written for students to help them understand their love languages. This book will not only help you discover your love language but also help you uncover ways to express yourself to your family, friends, and to the persons you date.

When chocolate met peanut butter, the delicious Reese's® Peanut Butter Cup was created. When cookies were combined with cream, a wonderful ice cream was invented. Taking the passions of True Love Waits and adding expressions of *The Five Love Languages* results in an awesome display of God's ultimate desire for His creations. His wish from the beginning was for us to live and have a friendship with Him that was totally consumed in love.

As you read this book, enjoy, learn, and impact your world.

—Tony Rankin

How to Use This Book

This book is intended to impact your entire life and the relationships you have with family, friends, and the persons you date. Reading it is not going to be like schoolwork. It should be enjoyable, encouraging you to discover better ways to love those closest to you.

You can work through this book by yourself. Take a few minutes every day for about a month and finish the pages at your own speed. Find a quiet place and set aside a time each day to work on several pages. You may choose your bedroom, the back deck, or the library at school. Try to find a time that will work for you every day and stay in a routine until you are finished.

You can work on this study with a group of friends at church. Ask your youth minister or small-group leader to take five Wednesdays or Sundays to lead you and your friends to complete the study together. Always take your book with the pages complete so you can maximize the time in the group for discussing your answers. There are some pages in the back to help a leader know how to use the information to lead interesting and enjoyable discussions.

Your youth minister might choose to use the book on a retreat or during a DiscipleNow weekend. That would work great too!

In this study you will find spaces to write answers, instructions to e-mail your responses to someone else, instructions to tell somebody something, and occasions when you will be asked to journal some of your personal thoughts. Read the entire book and follow the instructions to find better ways to love in life!

LOOKING FOR LOVE

1

I CAN'T STAND TO NOT BE IN LOVE

with somebody. It seems like I feel better if I know somebody loves me.
—Andrew, age 17

It's hard to find love these days! Everywhere I go it seems that love is defined differently, and I'm not sure I want to take the chance when I might find the wrong kind in the wrong place.
—Rachel, age 15

My day goes faster when I have a girlfriend. Feeling loved makes you look forward to getting done with homework and chores. —Stanley, age 16

I'm not sure my parents or friends care about me. What is it about me that makes me unlovable? —Amy, age 13

Everybody is looking for love—from somebody or somewhere! Some students look for it through the Internet while others try meeting people at the mall or at the skating rink. Some students pursue love through dating while others are fully content with having their love tank filled by their families.

List some other places teenagers look for love. _____

_____

Circle the things you turn to in order to find love:

Sports	Internet	Drugs	Alcohol
School	Chat rooms	Grades	Telephone
Family	Friends	Opposite sex	Social events
Books	Parents	Movies	Mall
Church	Sex	Parties	Music

Our need for love is important because it affects every area of our life. Imagine that you have this tank inside that can be filled only with love. When your love tank is empty, you feel as if nobody cares. You are less likely to be motivated when you do not feel loved. An empty love tank also affects your ability to empathize with others. When you do not feel loved, you have greater difficulty realizing how your negative actions might affect someone else's feelings.

Draw a line on the fuel gauge that indicates how full or empty your love tank is.

Is the empty light on? Have you recently gone in for a fill-up? Use the space below to write how well your friends and family are doing at helping you feel loved. If you have a boy/girlfriend, indicate how much he or she makes you feel valued and appreciated as well.

Friends _____

_____

_____

_____

Family _____

_____

_____

_____

Boy/Girlfriend _____

_____

List the names of your friends and family members (and boy/girlfriend if you have one) that you e-mail. Then write their e-mail addresses next to their names. You will be using these throughout this study._____

_____

_____

_____

_____

_____

_____

_____

_____

_____

_____

How are you doing expressing your love to your friends and family? On a scale of 1-10—with 1 being "I'm doing a horrible job!" and 10 being "I couldn't be doing better"—rate yourself on the Love Giving Scales below. If you have a boy/girlfriend, rate how well you show godly love to him or her as well.

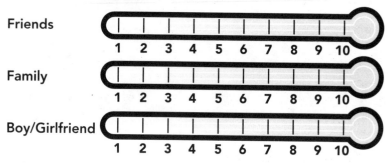

Friends
1 2 3 4 5 6 7 8 9 10

Family
1 2 3 4 5 6 7 8 9 10

Boy/Girlfriend
1 2 3 4 5 6 7 8 9 10

Having your love tank filled and filling others' tanks are closely related.

Ever feel lonely or unloved? What do you wish people would do for you during those times that would make you feel more loved? _____

_____

_____

_____

If you can't or won't write it out, draw a symbol or write down a word that represents the emptiness you feel. Getting honest with yourself is the first important step to finding appropriate love and being able to give it away.

The Bible shows examples of how people have looked for love in a variety of ways. Some have looked for it through companionship or sexual relationships, while others have searched for it by competing for power and control. People today look for love in exactly the same ways people in the Bible did.

Love Is More Than Skin Deep

Rahab, David, the Samaritan woman, and the woman the men wanted to stone all sought love in sexually scandalous ways. Look up these passages and match the persons with what they were involved in.

1. Joshua 2:1-7   a. Lust

2. 2 Samuel 11:2-5   b. Adultery

3. John 4:1-24   c. A series of bad relationships

4. John 8:1-11   d. Selling sex for money

Why do you think so many people look for love in sexual relationships? _____

_____

Kimber always has a boyfriend. If she breaks up with one, she doesn't feel happy until she finds another. Know anyone like her?

The truth is, it is easy to be carried away by romance and to mistake lust for love. The rush associated with sexual feelings is enough to lure many students toward a false sense of love. The problem with being in love with romance is that it is short-lived. "Charm is deceptive and beauty is fleeting" (Prov. 31:30).

Love is not sex. Sex is right and good when it is shared in a relationship of total commitment between a man and a woman in marriage. But don't confuse love and sex. In fact, sex before marriage often destroys whatever love exists in a relationship.

Some Friends Love the Right Way

Jonathan sought love by being a good friend. Read 1 Samuel 18:3-4 and notice what Jonathan did to express love to David.

The companionship of true friends is a great place to find acceptance, value, and love. A true friend seeks the best for you and doesn't place selfish demands or expectations on you. Unfortunately, some friendships are manipulative, self-serving, and unhealthy. Write an example of a friendship you know of that doesn't seem loving._____

_____

_____

Family Is the Right Place to Find Love

God designed the family to be the primary place where we can find love. But ever since Adam and Eve appeared on the scene and messed with God's perfect plan, families have experienced conflict. The Bible gives many examples of people receiving comfort from family. However, it also gives examples of rivalry and strife.

Skim over Genesis 27; then read Genesis 27:41. Describe the relationship between Jacob and Esau. _____

_____

_____

What about Joseph's family? Look up his story in Genesis 37. What evidence of love do you find? _____

_____

_____

_____

You may feel that your family is a lot like these families. There may be more tension and fighting than love. Fortunately, it is possible for families that have problems to become places of love.

When Joseph was placed in a position of power, he struggled with choosing appropriate ways of showing love. Write the demonstrations of love found in the following passage.

Genesis 45:1-15 _____
_____
_____
_____

Hugging your brother, sister, and parents after they have wronged you or you have hurt them is a wonderful way to express your love to your family and feel loved in return. Your family may not be the hugging kind. Still, there is something good about showing love to each other in ways that may seem a little over-the-top.

Love Cannot Be Found in Things

Lane had found a great way to deal with her empty love tank. She conned her dad out of his credit card and headed to the mall. A new pair of shoes always made her feel better.

This may seem ridiculous, but some of us really do try to fill our love tank with stuff.

The rich young ruler showed us how his "stuff" got in the way of loving God. (See Luke 18:18-23.) What did Jesus say about material wealth and love? Read Matthew 6:24.

_____
_____
_____

Acquiring stuff can be a vicious cycle. New things may make us feel good for a short time, but this quickly wears off. The toys, electronics, cars, and clothes eventually become obsolete or outdated. Then there is this incredible need to get newer things. And the cycle just continues, leaving us unfulfilled.

Love is found in relationships with God and with other people, not in the gaining of more stuff.

So What Is Love?

Love is caring for others and being valued by others. Love is being connected, accepted, and cared for.

Most of us want to be **connected.** As much as we want to be different and do things our way, we still want to know that others are there for us and want to be around us. We feel connected when we let others know our thoughts and desires. We can do this verbally or without saying a word.

How do you communicate love with your words? _____

_____

_____

What are some ways that you project love by your actions, without saying anything?_____

_____

_____

_____

We also feel loved when we are **accepted.** Being accepted helps us know that we are liked. We feel honored for who we are, respected for what we do well, and forgiven when we mess up. The opposite of acceptance is rejection.

What makes you feel accepted?_____

_____

_____

_____

What does rejection feel like and when has it happened to you recently?_____

_____

_____

_____

One of the coolest aspects of love is being **cared for.** It feels wonderful to be encouraged, to have people who are concerned for us, and to be protected. The opposite of being cared for is being abused.

If you have been abused, tell an adult who loves you. You should not carry this secret around and hide your pain. You deserve better than that! If you don't feel that you can tell a teacher, youth minister, youth leader, or school counselor, call the number listed in your local phone book for the Department of Human Resources or access the Web site *www.kidsafe-caps.org*.

What's the Point?

Students who do not have their love needs met by loving parents, supportive friends, caring youth leaders, or healthy dating relationships will go looking for love in all the wrong places.

What are some things students do because they don't feel loved?

☐ Make threats at school   ☐ Join gangs
☐ Have sex before marriage   ☐ Have a baby
☐ Shoot their parents   ☐ Drink alcoholic beverages
☐ Look at pornography   ☐ Use drugs
☐ Start rumors about others   ☐ Flirt too much

If you're serious about wanting the best for your friends and family, make it your business to keep their love tanks full. You may not feel like your own love tank is full. The paradox is, when you focus on showing others love, you end up having a lot of love poured into you.

Read 1 Corinthians 13:4-7 and list ways mentioned to love.

_____

_____

_____

Now read Romans 12:9-21 and consider how attitude impacts the way we express love.

Pretend you are an advice columnist answering a teen's question about inappropriate expressions of "love." Write an answer based on what this passage says about real love for others.

Dear _____ ,

_____

_____

_____

_____

_____

_____

_____

_____

_____

_____

_____

_____

_____

_____

_____

_____

Sincerely,

_____

These passages are filled with great advice about love. Do you notice thoughts about patience, forgiveness, rudeness, forever, sincerity, cursing, or paybacks? _____

_____

_____

Go back and reread the passages, thinking carefully about these instructions as they relate to loving your family, friends, and dates.

What Shape Are You In to Love or Be Loved?

All of us need to be loved. Love is the main building block of relationships. When love is real, it is spoken at all times, in all situations, and everywhere. The better you communicate love, the healthier your relationships will be.

Love doesn't fix everything, but it sure makes the anticipation of the future more hopeful. Love is not the answer to everything, but it sure does make difficult issues easier to handle. Love combined with caring people helps us like ourselves more, feel more important, and feel safer in a chaotic world.

Find time every day to work on your relationships; discover your own love needs and languages; and enjoy physical, emotional, and sexual purity.

Weekly Observations

While watching television this week, notice some examples of people looking for love. List the situations below.

Commercials _____

_____

Movies _____

_____

Sports _____

_____

Situation Comedies _____

_____

Nature/History Channel _____

_____

News Programs _____

_____

Others _____

_____

What needs of affection, admiration, or love did you hear in the music you listened to this week? (It could have been right or wrong, good or bad.)

_____

_____

_____

_____

While spending time with your friends, family, or boy/girlfriend this week, what did you hear them say they needed in order to feel loved?

_____
_____
_____
_____
_____

Look back at the e-mail list you wrote on page 9. If you have access to a computer, e-mail several of these people and tell them how much you love them. Include a specific thing you will do for them because of your appreciation for who they are and what they mean to you. (And then make sure you do it, or they will think you are a fake!)

Prayer

Write a prayer that expresses your need for love. Ask God for specific things that you are looking for from people around you. Remember, asking works a lot better than demanding.

_____
_____
_____
_____
_____
_____
_____
_____
_____
_____
_____

Journal Entry

Date _____

It would feel loving to me if _____
(person's name)

would_____.
(action)

Realizing my need for love helps me recognize... _____

_____

_____

_____

_____

_____

_____

_____

_____

_____

_____

One thing I will do to demonstrate love to a friend this week is... _____

_____

_____

_____

_____

_____

_____

_____

_____

_____

_____

_____

This week, tell your parents that you love them and that you need them to love you. How and when will you tell them?

_____
_____
_____
_____
_____
_____
_____
_____

One way I can express love this week to my boy/girlfriend (without saying "I love you") is... _____
_____
_____
_____
_____
_____
_____

Love is an action, not a feeling. For me this means... _____
_____
_____
_____
_____
_____
_____
_____
_____
_____
_____

2

UNDERSTANDING LOVE LANGUAGES

THE MOST FUNDAMENTAL NEED
of teenagers is feeling loved. Loving
and being loved motivates teenagers
to fully enjoy life's circumstances.
The five languages of love are words
of affirmation, physical touch, quality
time, acts of service, and gifts.
—from *The Five Love Languages of Teenagers*
by Gary Chapman

Have you been in an airport lately? Imagine you are in an airport and hear "American Airlines announcing the final call for flight 237 at gate 14B." Then you hear "American Airlines anuncia la última llamada del vuelo 237 en la puerta de salida número 14B." People communicate and understand many different languages. You probably know students at school who speak two or more languages.

List below all of the languages that are spoken or taught at your school. _____
_____
_____

Music is considered a universal language. There is a lady who has a dog that loves bluegrass! Music is a common thread at religious gatherings, cultural shows, and international events such as the Olympics. But even music has limitations in effectively communicating with everybody. You probably cringe when your dad decides to play his favorite CDs.

Someone once said, "Love makes the world go around." Love really is the only universal language. Whether people are from China or Canada, whether they are 6 or 60, they respond to real, genuine love.

What are ways that people express love? _____
_____
_____
_____

You may have mentioned kisses, high-fives, gifts, hugs, phone calls, or spending time together. There are many kinds of ways to express love, affection, or appreciation. Unfortunately, we don't all express or understand love in the same way.

Consider these situations:

Someone you hardly know gives you a big hug. Do you feel loved or uncomfortable? _____

_____

Your mom asks you to take a drive with her. You ask where you are going. She says, "No place in particular. I just want to spend some time with you." Do you feel loved or that this is a big waste of time? _____

_____

While you're at camp, your brother decides to paint your bedroom. He chooses your favorite color and spends most of the week trying to make it look nice. Do you feel loved or are you frustrated that he invaded your space? _____

_____

You and your sister have a big fight after she ruined your favorite shirt. Your sister gives you a gift certificate to your favorite store. Do you feel loved or that she is trying to buy your forgiveness? _____

_____

Your dad tells you to mow the yard because he doesn't have time to do it this week. When you are finished, he compliments you on a job well done and tells you how special you are for doing such a good job. Do you feel loved or do you wish he'd given you money? _____

_____

The point is that all of us give and receive love in ways that feel right to us.

Use the letters of your name to create an acrostic about what makes you feel loved. An example is done for you.

Do fun things with someone.

Rent a movie together.

Enjoy fishing with me.

Wash my truck with me.

Now you try it!

We all want to be loved! If you could Instant Message™ someone on your computer right now, what would you say about what makes you feel loved? What could the person do to help you feel loved? Write your message to the person.

_____

_____

_____

_____

_____

_____

Find Your Love Language

Often we try to love other people like we want to be loved. In other words, we speak our own love language to others because we don't know their main love language. But our friends and family may not have the same main love language as we do. As a result, when we feel like we are showing love to them, they may not be receiving it as love.

Some people feel loved with <u>words of affirmation</u> while others want <u>gifts</u>. Some like <u>quality time</u> or <u>acts of service</u> while others choose <u>physical touch</u>. Which one of these five do you think you want the most? Circle it above.

Take the following test (Don't worry it's not as bad as school!) so you can find out how you like to receive love. It will help you and the people you love know how to love better.

On the next 2 pages you will read 30 pairs of statements. Ask yourself, *Which of these do I prefer?* You may enjoy both expressions of love, but you must choose only one of them. Circle the letter at the end of the statement you choose. For example, if you feel that "I like one-to-one time" describes you better than "I feel loved when someone gives practical help to me," draw a circle around the *B* beside the first statement.

As you work through this profile, think of a significant person in your life, such as a parent, close friend, or a boy/girlfriend. When you have finished, count how many of each letter you circled and record the totals at the bottom of page 28.

Don't complete the profile when you are wiped out, tired from studying, or in a bad mood. After you finish, get a parent, friend, or date to take the profile to find their main love languages.

Five Love Languages Profile

1. I like to receive notes of affirmation.   A
   I like to be hugged.   E

2. I like one-to-one time.   B
   I feel loved when someone gives practical help to me.   D

3. I like it when I get gifts.   C
   I like taking long walks with someone.   B

4. I feel loved when I get help.   D
   I feel loved when I'm touched.   E

5. I feel loved when I receive an embrace.   E
   I feel loved when I receive a gift.   C

6. I like to go places with someone.   B
   I like to hold hands.   E

7. Visible symbols of love (gifts) are very important to me.   C
   I feel loved when I am affirmed.   A

8. I like to sit close.   E
   I like to be told I am attractive.   A

9. I like to spend time with someone.   B
   I like to receive little gifts.   C

10. Words of acceptance are important to me.   A
    I know I am loved when I receive help.   D

11. I like to be with someone when I do things.   B
    I like to receive kind words.   A

12. What someone does affects me more than what he or she says.   D
    I feel whole when I am hugged.   E

13. I value praise and try to avoid criticism.   A
    Several small gifts mean more to me than one large gift.   C

14. I feel close while talking or doing something with someone.   B
    I feel closer to someone when he or she touches me often.   E

15. I like to be complimented for my achievements.   A
    I feel loved when someone does things for me that he doesn't enjoy.   D

16. I like to be touched when someone walks by.   E
    I like to be listened to sympathetically.   B

17. I feel loved when someone helps me with my chores. — D
    I really enjoy receiving gifts. — C
18. I like to be complimented on my appearance. — A
    I feel loved when someone takes time to understand my feelings. — B
19. I feel secure when I am being touched. — E
    Acts of service make me feel loved. — D
20. I appreciate the many things someone does for me. — D
    I like receiving homemade gifts. — C
21. I really enjoy getting undivided attention. — B
    I really enjoy someone doing some act of service for me. — D
22. I feel loved when my birthday is celebrated with a gift. — C
    I feel loved when my birthday is celebrated with meaningful words. — A
23. I know someone is thinking of me when he or she gives me a gift. — C
    I feel loved when I get help with chores. — D
24. I appreciate it when someone listens patiently to me. — B
    I appreciate it when someone remembers special days with a gift. — C
25. I like to know someone cares enough to help with my daily tasks. — D
    I enjoy extended trips with someone. — B
26. An unexpected kiss on the cheek makes me feel loved. — E
    Getting an unexpected gift for no special occasion excites me. — C
27. I like to be told that I am appreciated. — A
    I like to be looked at when I am talking to someone. — B
28. Gifts are always special to me. — C
    I feel good when I am being touched. — E
29. I feel loved when someone enthusiastically does a task I have requested. — D
    I feel loved when someone tells me how much he appreciates me. — A
30. I need to be touched every day. — E
    I need words of affirmation daily. — A

Totals: A ____   B ____   C ____   D ____   E ____

Figure Your Score

A=Words of Affirmation
B=Quality Time
C=Gifts
D=Acts of Service
E=Physical Touch

Your highest score shows your main love language. The next highest score is the next important thing to you. If the scores are the same, you are bilingual. (Your Spanish teacher would be proud!) The highest possible score for any love language is 12.

My main love language is_____.

My next important love language is_____.

Get the picture? Figuring this out may help explain some of your past behaviors and choices. Think back over your past and ask yourself, *What have I most often demanded from others?*

Finding out about your main love language will help you earn extra credit with your parents, make friendships easier, and enhance your dating experiences. How could this be? Write down what you think could happen now that you know your love language. _____

_____
_____
_____
_____
_____
_____

Most importantly, having a clear understanding of your primary and secondary love languages can make your future a blast!

You will feel more loved when the people closest to you know what your love language is. And you can best know how to respond to them if you know what their love languages are.

Ask your parents, siblings, best friend, and boy/girlfriend, if you have one, to complete the same survey you just took. Ask them to use a different color of ink to indicate their answers. Write down their love languages in the space below.

Name	Love Language
_____	_____
_____	_____
_____	_____
_____	_____
_____	_____
_____	_____
_____	_____

Look below to see what you and others desire most when it comes to feeling loved.

- **Words of Affirmation**—spoken words, written cards or letters, e-mails, compliments

- **Quality Time**—trips, walks, talking at home, undivided attention, one-to-one conversations

- **Gifts**—celebration of special occasions; small, sentimental gifts; things you have made

- **Acts of Service**—assistance with chores, kept promises, helping in little ways

- **Physical Touch**—hugs, sitting close, back rubs, pats on the back

Don't Accept Lies About Love

So many people are hungry to be loved. Imagine what our world would be like if we all were able to express love in the ways other persons needed.

Students often turn to sexual behaviors because they desperately want to feel loved. They don't realize that the consequences of these behaviors are destructive, long-lasting, and often nonreversible. These sexual behaviors are only temporary thrills and have nothing to do with real love.

Feelings can trick you. Sexual behavior can feel so right but be so wrong! Name a time when what you thought was true love really wasn't. _____

_____

You probably have at least one friend who has already experienced some of the negative consequences of sex before marriage. Mark the consequences he or she experienced.

☐ **Broken heart**   ☐ **Guilt**
☐ **Bad reputation**   ☐ **STD**
☐ **Pregnancy**   ☐ **Depression**
☐ **Shame**   ☐ **Untrusting heart**

The ecstasy of sexual pleasure is an incredible gift from God, but one which is to be "opened" only after we are married. In today's world, delaying sexual gratification may not make sense. But we must trust God and the people who love us when they say that true love waits for the best time and the right relationship—marriage.

Love as Jesus Loved

Jesus loved perfectly. The Bible records Jesus showing us how and when to love other people.

Match each of the following passages with the specific love language Jesus demonstrated. Consult the explanations of the love languages below for help as needed.

1. Matthew 16:17-19   a. Gifts

2. Mark 1:16-20   b. Acts of Service

3. Mark 1:41   c. Quality Time

4. Mark 8:1-8   d. Words of Affirmation

5. John 13:3-5   e. Physical Touch

 Words of Affirmation encourage, not manipulate for selfish pleasure.

 Quality Time means being willing to give a part of our life and schedule away.

 Gifts are just that, gifts. We mustn't expect anything in return for our efforts.

 Acts of Service are not forced by others but instead spring from an internal motivation to help. They are freely given, not a means of manipulation.

 Physical Touch is a basic expression of love but must be expressed in the appropriate way at the appropriate time.

☀ Words of Affirmation—Express words of appreciation for the things you like about the other person. List some things you like about your family members and friends. _____

_____

_____

🕐 Quality Time—Quality time means togetherness. It doesn't mean having to be right next to each other at all times, but rather focused attention. List some things your family and friends like to do with you. _____

_____

_____

💎 Gifts—They don't have to be expensive. They might not cost anything or even be material objects. What are some things you could give that would say, "I love you"?_____

_____

_____

☂ Acts of Service—Some family members and friends feel loved when you do things for them. Examples: helping with homework, lending a DVD, or helping with a chore. List an act of service you could do to demonstrate love._____

_____

_____

🤝 Physical Touch—Touch that expresses love is not about gratifying yourself. Neither is it about responding to the sexual feelings of another. It is all about showing genuine affection through caring and healthy touch. What things should you do and not do to demonstrate your love to people in your life? _____

_____

_____

Jot Down Good Ideas

During your class, other students will share how others have best met their needs for love. Write below some of the best ideas as they are shared to help you express love well to your family members and friends.

Words of Affirmation _____

_____

_____

_____

Quality Time _____

_____

_____

_____

Gifts _____

_____

_____

_____

Acts of Service _____

_____

_____

_____

Physical Touch _____

_____

_____

_____

Weekly Observations

📺 While watching television this week, notice examples of all five love languages. List them below.

• Words of Affirmation _____

_____

• Quality Time _____

_____

• Gifts _____

_____

• Acts of Service _____

_____

• Physical Touch _____

_____

🎺 What needs of affection, admiration, or love did you hear in the music you listened to this week? (It could have been right or wrong, good or bad.) _____

_____

_____

_____

😈 While spending time with your friends, family, or a boy/girlfriend this week, what did you hear them say they needed in order to feel loved? _____

_____

_____

_____

Look back at the e-mail list you wrote on page 9. If you have access to a computer, e-mail several of these people and tell them how much you love them. Include a specific thing you will do for them because of your appreciation for who they are and what they mean to you.

Learning to love appropriately and being open to being loved appropriately requires that you recognize the five love languages. Based on the knowledge you gained when your family and friends took the profile, start loving them in a way that they most appreciate. Get creative, use energy, and do things differently to better love those around you.

Prayer

Ask God to help you learn to love better. Thank Jesus for being the perfect example of how to love. Thank God for the ultimate love He showed when He allowed Jesus to die for you on the cross.

 **Journal Entry**

Date _____

Knowing my main love language helps me realize...

_____
_____
_____
_____

One thing I will do to demonstrate love to a friend this week is... _____

_____
_____
_____

Now that I know my parents' main love languages, I will...

_____
_____
_____
_____

True love means waiting until your wedding night to express love sexually. For me this means... _____

_____
_____
_____
_____
_____
_____

LOVING
YOUR FAMILY

I NEVER REALIZED HOW MUCH

my parents really loved me until I told them how afraid I was. —Ed, age 16

The best part of homework is when Mom comes by and rubs my shoulders. I forget all about algebra. It relaxes me. —Barrett, age 16

I know my folks love me because they do so many things for me. Mom takes me to cheerleader practice and to all the games. Daddy helps me with my homework, especially my math, which I hate. —Krystal, age 14

My dad doesn't hug me as much as he used to. I don't know if he thinks I'm too adult now and don't need it. But I miss his hugs. They always make me feel so special. —Meredith, age 15

Do Parents Really Care?
Which family is most like yours? (Check the appropriate box.)

☐ I have parents who do a great job of showing me uncondi-
tional love. When times are difficult, they demonstrate faith,
mercy, forgiveness, and encouragement. When times are
good, they laugh, encourage, and celebrate each other's
accomplishments. My siblings are fun to be around, and we
play and interact with each other often. That doesn't mean
we never have disagreements, but for the most part we are
pleasant around one another.

☐ I have a family that doesn't fight much, but we also don't
spend much time together. We don't argue all the time, but
we don't have fun either. We are extremely busy and rarely
eat together. It seems that we are all disconnected from
each other.

☐ I am in a family that is at war. There is a lot of yelling, fussing,
and arguing. My parents don't seem to care about me. They
do not speak kindly nor do they remember special occasions. They do not hug me or encourage me. They do not have
time for me and rarely participate in my school or church activities. My siblings are mean; and we fight, too.

Maybe your family doesn't fit into one particular category. Under-
line or highlight any words that describe your family. You may
have things marked in all three scenarios. All families need to
work on the way they love one another. Read on to find help.

Do You Feel Trapped in Your Family?

Television programs have examples of both good and chaotic families.

List examples of TV shows in which families display good values and healthy relationships. _____

_____

_____

_____

Can you think of TV families that are bad models for teenagers to pattern their future relationships after? Write them in the space below. _____

_____

_____

_____

The family is like a petri dish. Throw in a dad, a mom, and a couple of kids; then watch the friction. You can't live in the petri dish with people and not find out the good—and the bad—about them. It is in that petri dish that you learn some of your most important life skills. For example, you learn to relate to other people by the relationships you form with your parents and your siblings. Scary, huh?

Girls, want to know how a guy will end up treating you? Watch how he treats his mom. You say you can't get along with your little brother? You'd better learn, because you are going to be dealing with people like him the rest of your life.

Family is also the most significant place you learn to express love. Your parents may be more like the Osbournes than the Cleavers, but they still were the first ones to show you love. And they were the first people you tried to show love to in return.

What are the most significant ways your parents have shown you love? _____
_____
_____
_____

Be careful here. Often the things that make you the most angry at your parents are really expressions of love.

Which of the following do you think your parents worry about? (Check all that apply.)

☐ Your peers won't accept you.
☐ You will become pregnant or get someone pregnant.
☐ You will make poor choices with the friends you hang with.
☐ You will become addicted to pornography, drugs, or alcohol.
☐ You will not spend your time wisely.
☐ You will embarrass yourself or your family.
☐ You will wreck your life.
☐ You will become irresponsible.

Parents are far from perfect; but many times their restrictions and rules—and even their scolding and yelling—are motivated by their desire for you to live a full, rich life.

Want to add any significant ways your parents show you love?

_____
_____
_____
_____
_____
_____

Love Is a Part of Anger

In the minds of most people, love and anger are antonyms—they just don't seem to go together. In reality, they are opposite sides of the same coin. Love seeks the good of the other person and so does rightly directed anger. We experience anger when we encounter what we perceive to be wrong behavior on the part of others. Parents get angry with their teenager when the teen does or says something that the parents consider to be irresponsible. Teenagers get angry with their parents when the parents behave in a way the teens consider to be unfair or self-serving.

The purpose of anger is to motivate us to take loving action; that is, to do something to try to turn the teenager or parent in the right direction. Unfortunately, many of us have never learned to take such loving action, and we end up taking destructive action.[1]

Have You Ever Wanted to Be a Model?

God's intention for the family is that it be a place where people experience the kind of love God has for each person. You may be thinking, *My family is not exactly scoring 100 on that!* Fair enough. You can't change your parents into model parents or your siblings into model brothers and sisters. But, are *you* showing God's love to them?

Read Ephesians 6:1-3. Write the passage in your own words.

_____

_____

_____

_____

_____

Obey your parents means to be guided by their instructions. Your parents will give you directions (most of the time this is because they love you). Your love for them will be demonstrated by your response to their requests (and even demands at times).

What instructions are hard for you to obey? _____
_____
_____
_____

List two ways that you could be more loving in response to your parents' rules or guidelines.

1. _____
_____
2. _____
_____

Another word in this passage is *honor*. *Honor* means "to regard with respect."

How can you honor your parents?_____
_____
_____
_____

Many times these words (*obey* and *honor*) are the beginning of fights and not the start of more love. Anger develops as a response to feeling mistreated or in opposition to another person or his opinions. Like love, anger is expressed in many languages and tones of voice.

Read 1 John 4:7-12. How did God show love to you?
_____
_____

How are you supposed to express love to others (including your mean parents and ornery little sister)?
_____
_____

Lose the Attitude!

What could you do to demonstrate love to a family member instead of raging or losing it? Think back to the five love languages and list an example for each that would be a positive expression of love instead of a negative act of anger.

Words of Affirmation _____
_____

Quality Time _____
_____

Gifts _____
_____

Acts of Service _____
_____

Physical Touch _____
_____

One of the greatest fears that parents have concerns the way their teenager expresses his or her love to persons of the opposite sex. Some of the biggest conflicts you will have with your parents may involve dating, flirting, relationships, sexual behavior, pregnancy, or pornography.

Read Proverbs 7 and record in the blanks below what the passage says about love and purity.

Keep my commands and _____. (v. 2)

Protect my _____ as you would the pupil of your eye. (v. 2)

Wisdom will _____
_____. (v. 5)

According to verse 7, what got the young man in trouble? __
_____
_____
_____
_____
_____

The seductions of verses 10-19 include... _____
_____
_____
_____
_____
_____

In verse 21, _____**and** _____
influenced the young man.

Then she had him. He gave in to her seductions, and he was like a deer walking into a noose.

Loving parents want you to run from sexual dangers. Trust them.

How to Say "I Love You" to Your Family

List below each member of your family and his or her love language. Refer back to page 30 if necessary. Then write a few ways to show love to each of them. Look at the suggestions on page 47 for ideas.

Name:_____ Love Language:_____
My love response: _____
_____
_____
_____

Name:_____ Love Language:_____
My love response: _____
_____
_____
_____

Name:_____ Love Language:_____
My love response: _____
_____
_____
_____

Name:_____ Love Language:_____
My love response: _____
_____
_____
_____

Name:_____ Love Language:_____
My love response: _____
_____
_____
_____

☀ Words of Affirmation

Say, "Thanks for cooking supper." "I like the way you moved the furniture." "I'm lucky to have a brother who drives me to school." "I'm glad you didn't change jobs so we don't have to change schools." "You are good at coaching." "I couldn't have performed in this recital without your help." "Tell me other stories about my grandparents." "You are really smart when it comes to...."

◷ Quality Time

Go for a drive. Play an enjoyable board game. Enjoy family vacations. Watch a movie together. Ride together when you go to church. Be willing to go to your sister's favorite restaurant without complaining. Take a walk around the block together.

◇ Gifts

Give your mom a coupon book of chores you are willing to do. Wrap up a brownie and put it in your sister's lunch box. Cut from magazines pictures of gifts you wish you could buy for your parents.

☂ Acts of Service

Volunteer to do a chore. Clean your mom's car. Cook breakfast for your dad. Give your mom a "night off" from washing the dishes. Pick up your dirty clothes and put them in the laundry room.

🤝 Physical Touch

Kiss a family member on the cheek. Shadow box with a brother. Rub your sister's back. Wrestle fairly with a younger sibling. Lean on your parent while watching TV. High-five each other after a ball game. Pat a sibling on the back after a good or bad report card.

Your family plays an important role in the development of your love life. Filling your life with words of affirmation, acts of service, quality time, appropriate touch, and gifts can replace some of the negative feelings in your family. It can also replace shallow and meaningless family relationships with ones that are long-lasting and significant.

The next time you hear your parent or sibling say the following statements, think about what they really mean. Write your understanding of what is really being said after each statement.

"We want you home by 10:30 tonight because you are tired."
_____
_____

"We will leave the lights on for you when you come home."
_____
_____

"Make sure you let us know when you get home."_____
_____
_____

"Call us if you need us."_____
_____
_____

"Tell us about your date." _____
_____
_____

"Can you do something with us on Thursday instead of going out with her again?" _____
_____
_____

Weekly Observations

While viewing television this week, watch for a great example of how you wish your family loved one another. Write down the name of the show that you watched.

_____

What was so great about the way they loved one another?

_____
_____
_____
_____
_____
_____

What one thing about the parents on the show do you want to model when you are a parent?_____
_____

How well did the siblings get along? _____
_____
_____
_____
_____

What needs for family relationships and attention did you hear this week while listening to a CD or the radio? (It could have been right or wrong, good or bad.)

_____
_____
_____
_____

While spending time with a friend, family member, or boy/girlfriend this week, what did you hear the person say he or she needed in order to feel loved by his or her family? _____

_____
_____
_____
_____
_____
_____
_____
_____
_____
_____
_____
_____
_____
_____
_____
_____
_____

Take a look at the e-mail list you made on page 9. If you have access to a computer, write to your parents and tell them how much you love them and include a specific thing you will do for them because of your appreciation for who they are and what they mean to you. (This may be the first time you say or show them that you love them. Don't worry if you feel a little nervous. You'll be glad you told them!)

Prayer
Ask God to help you be more thankful for your family. Commit yourself in prayer to do a better job at showing your love by your words, actions, gifts, and responses to your parents and siblings.

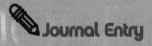 **Journal Entry**

Date _____

It would feel loving to me if my parent would... (Write an action.) _____
_____
_____
_____

One thing I will do to demonstrate love to my parent or sibling this week is... _____
_____
_____

One thing my parent said or did this week that indicates he or she understands what I have tried to work on this week is...
_____
_____

One way I can say, "I love you" to my family (without using these words) this week is... _____
_____
_____
_____

Parents speak a different language than students do. For me this means... _____
_____
_____
_____

1. Adapted from Gary Chapman, *The Five Love Languages of Teenagers* (Chicago: Northfield Publishing, 2000), 39.

LOVING YOUR FRIENDS

TRUE FRIENDS STAND WITH YOU

and hold your hand when you feel the worst. —Heather, age 15

A teenager's desire to be with friends is not a rejection of parents; it is evidence that his social horizons are widening beyond the family. —from *The Five Love Languages of Teenagers* by Dr. Gary Chapman

Melissa and Todd have been friends since second grade. Their parents are friends at church, and occasionally the two families get together to cook out or go to a ball game. The two friends tell each other their secrets. They laugh together, cry over hurts and disappointments, and discuss future college and work plans. One night after Todd broke up with his girlfriend, he was tempted to become too physical with Melissa. As he considered the temptation, he tried to justify things in his mind. *She already knows everything about me. We are already close. She obviously cares for me. This would be just a one-time thing.* So Todd…

How would you finish this story? _____

_____

_____

_____

_____

_____

What are the strengths of this relationship? _____

_____

_____

_____

What concerns would you have for this friendship? _____

_____

_____

_____

Friendships can exist for many reasons, but the main one has to be the need for a trustworthy companion who shares ideas and thoughts with no expectation for physical, or sexual, pleasure. Friendships are valuable and necessary for a good life. But good friendships must have boundaries so that they remain just that—friendships.

Benefit from Close Friendships

Many teenagers see their parents working long hours. As parents strive to provide for their families, they have difficulty cultivating friends and making time to relax and spend time with them. They are not modeling for their teenagers the value of having friends. Your generation has a choice to change this trend. Making the decision now to develop friendships that last forever is a smart move.

What is the big deal about having friends anyway? List four benefits here.

1. _____

2. _____

3. _____

4. _____

You might have listed benefits such as *friends are always there for me*, *like me regardless of my mood*, *encourage me*, and *spend time with me*. As you read this chapter, see if you can discover some new reasons for having friends and some characteristics of good friends. When you find them turn back to this page and write them in the box below.

More Reasons to Have Friends

- _____ - _____
- _____ - _____
- _____ - _____
- _____ - _____
- _____ - _____
- _____ - _____

The Bible gives us insight into relationships. Look at two good examples of friendship in Ruth 1:3-18 and 1 Samuel 18:1-3; 19:1-7. Choose one of these passages and answer the following questions.

What is happening in the story? _____

_____

_____

_____

How did the two friends meet? _____

_____

What was the key to making this relationship work? _____

_____

Do you have a relationship like this one? _____

_____

If not, what could you do to find someone like the "other friend" in this story? _____

_____

_____

What characteristics are you looking for in a friend? _____

_____

_____

What is good about these kinds of relationships? _____

_____

_____

Why do we need them? _____

_____

_____

Friends can...
- Be there for you when your family is unavailable.
- Comfort you when you are upset with your family.
- Listen to you express your ideas and feelings.
- Let you laugh at dumb jokes and cry with significant losses without calling you "crazy" or "immature."

How is a male-female relationship different? _____

_____

_____

Evaluate Your F.R.I.E.N.D.S

Good friendships take effort from both parties. Look at the following acrostic and decide whether you are this kind of friend and if you have a friend like this.

F ORGIVENESS. Good friends are able to find ways to forgive each other when something goes wrong. Forgiveness means not needing to blame anyone for a wrongdoing. Forgiveness affirms with words that give a sense of "I'm moving on and will not keep bringing this problem up."

What wrongs do you need to forgive some of your friends for?

_____

_____

_____

_____

When someone asks for forgiveness, forgive him or her. Forgiving others is a wonderful way to express love.

R IGHT TOUCHES. Friends develop good boundaries with each other. When we form a friendship with someone, we expect that certain physical touches will not occur, while others are appropriate.

What are some touches that ruin friendships? _____

_____

_____

_____

The trust that friendships are based on is strengthened when each person behaves in respectful ways. Once we cross the physical or sexual line, it is impossible to come back and pretend it never happened. The friendship may be over at that point. If it's not over, it will never be the same. Boundaries are there to protect a relationship, not to restrict or exclude.

INTEREST IN SPENDING TIME TOGETHER. True friends look for ways to spend time with each other. Time spent together not only validates the relationship but also gives it opportunity to grow. Quality time reminds the other person that he or she is a priority for you. It is nearly impossible to get to know a friend better when you rarely spend time with him or her.

What kinds of things do you enjoy doing with your friends?

_____

_____

_____

_____

Sometimes we need to spend time with same-sexed friends. What's cool about same-sexed friends? _____

_____

_____

_____

What can you do with same-sexed friends that you cannot do with those of the opposite sex? _____

_____

_____

What friends in the Bible enjoyed spending time with each other? _____
_____
_____

ENJOY GIVING. Although we should never give something to someone in order to receive something in return, giving is a part of friendship. Expensive gifts are not necessary. Giving time to listen or giving small gifts of thanks can be as meaningful as diamonds and huge gift certificates.

What would you enjoy getting from a friend? _____
_____
_____
_____

Name three of your friends and think of a gift that doesn't cost anything that you could give each of them. When will you do it? Write the date next to the gift.

Name	Gift	Date

DO THINGS. Doing acts of service for a friend is a part of any great relationship. Finding out ways to help or provide assistance can enhance a relationship.

What could you do this week to show someone that you care for him or her and value his or her friendship? _____
_____
_____
_____
_____

What act would be helpful to you? _____

_____

_____

SHARE THOUGHTS. We can share our thoughts by speaking words of affirmation, writing notes of encouragement, and discussing different opinions.

Can you imagine not ever being encouraged, praised, valued, trusted, or cared for? What would it be like if no one said affirming things to you for an entire month? _____

_____

_____

_____

Have any of your friends expressed an opinion to you that you have a hard time accepting? Write about it below. _____

_____

_____

_____

_____

_____

Find some way this week to hear the person out without over-reacting. Find a way to affirm the person by saying something positive about him or her.

You probably recognized the five love languages in the description of real friends above. Deep and fast friendship really does depend on expressions of genuine love.

Some of your friends will be most touched when you give them a small gift; others will respond most to words of affirmation. All of these expressions of genuine love are important in building friendships.

Look at Friendships in the Bible

The Bible shows us many good examples of friendships. Read each passage below and match it to the love language shown between the friends.

1. Genesis 41:42-43   a. Words of Affirmation

2. Ruth 1:15-17   b. Quality Time

3. 1 Samuel 18:3-4   c. Gifts

4. 1 Kings 19:19-21   d. Acts of Service

5. Acts 6:6   e. Physical Touch

6. Acts 18:1-3

7. 2 Timothy 4:13

8. Philippians 1:3-5

Remember to Say Thanks

Saying thanks to a friend for his or her love is one way you can express affection. Take a few minutes to write a friend a letter and tell the person how much you appreciate him or her and why. You may want to include words of gratitude for a time when your friend helped you get through such events as your parents' divorce, a grandparent's death, a bad grade on a report card, or a failure of a dating relationship.

Dear _____,

_____
_____
_____
_____
_____
_____
_____
_____
_____
_____
_____
_____
_____
_____
_____
_____
_____
_____
_____
_____
_____
_____

Sincerely,

_____

Say "I Appreciate You" to Your Friends

List the names of your good friends below. If they haven't studied this book, get with them one at a time and read the 30 pairs of statements to them. Write on a separate sheet of paper their preferred answers and help them discover their primary and secondary love languages.

Beside each name below, write your friend's main love language. Remember to include your best friend. (Check page 30 if necessary.) Then write a loving response or two that the person would appreciate the most. Look at the suggestions on page 63 for some ideas.

Name:_____ Love Language:_____
My love response: _____
_____
_____
_____

Name:_____ Love Language:_____
My love response: _____
_____
_____
_____

Name:_____ Love Language:_____
My love response: _____
_____
_____
_____

Name:_____ Love Language:_____
My love response: _____
_____
_____
_____

Words of Affirmation

Say, "I'm lucky to have a friend like you." "Thanks for your help with my algebra." "I like the way you…." "You were awesome in the play." "I think you should keep singing in church. You are good." "You are one of the funniest guys in our class." "You are great at keeping a situation from getting out of hand."

 Quality Time

Hang out after school. Go to a ball game together. Go out to get a soft drink when your friend is having a tough time. Study together for a big test. Go for a ride in the car. Go for a walk.

 Gifts

Buy him a milk shake or sports drink. Give her a copy of a Christian devotional magazine. Give a small gift on a special occasion. Put a piece of candy in her locker and attach an encouraging note. Give a "gift" you made out of household items or leftover cafeteria paper and utensils (and then explain the significance).

Acts of Service

Help with homework for a hard class. Go to his house to help mow the grass. Carry her backpack. Help with his chores for the afternoon.

Physical Touch

Give high-fives at the ball game. Pat him on the back after hearing good news. Give her appropriate hugs that don't feel romantic. Rub his shoulders when he is stressed. Arm wrestle with him.

What Are You Doing?

What are you doing to help your friends feel loved and remain sexually pure? _____
_____
_____
_____
_____

Teenagers will listen to words of warning from a peer before they will listen to such words from a parent. Talk with your friends about secret sins and the danger of such sexual impurities as oral sex, intercourse, rubbing private body parts, and pornography.

Agree to hold one another accountable and often ask one another, "How well are you doing at staying pure sexually?"

Discuss with your friends "How far is too far?" Be prepared for difficult questions. If you don't know the answer, don't make something up. Ask your youth minister or a caring adult for wisdom and good advice.

Ecclesiastes 4:9-12 says two are better than one. Read the passage and write down a time when a friend's love helped you to stay strong in the face of temptation. _____
_____
_____
_____
_____

What can you do to help one of your friends stay pure? _____
_____
_____
_____
_____

Weekly Observations

📺 Numerous television shows and movies depict friendships. Some are healthy and some are not. List some you've seen that show friends interacting. _____

_____

_____

_____

_____

_____

What are the good qualities displayed in these relationships?

_____

_____

_____

What one thing about these friendships do you want to model with your friends? _____

_____

_____

🎺 Think about the lyrics of songs you've heard this week. Do any discuss the relationships between friends? If so, what words of affirmation, quality time, gifts, acts of service, and physical touch were mentioned? _____

_____

_____

_____

_____

_____

_____

_____

While spending time with your friends this week, what did you hear them say they needed in order to feel loved by their family or friends? _____

_____

_____

_____

_____

_____

Take a look at the e-mail list you made on page 9. If you have access to a computer, write to a friend and tell him how much you love him and include a specific thing you will do for him because of your appreciation for who he is and what he means to you. (This may seem strange and weird the first time you say or show the person that you love him. Don't worry if you feel a little nervous. You'll be glad you told him!) _____

_____

_____

_____

_____

_____

_____

Prayer

Ask God to help you be the friend He wants you to be. Mention your friends by name and share a prayer request that is specific to their lives. Pray for opportunities to love them at the right time.

"A friend loves at all times" (Prov. 17:17).
"There is a friend who stays closer than a brother" (Prov. 18:24).

 **Journal Entry**

Date _____

It would feel loving to me if my friend would... (Write an action.)_____
_____
_____
_____

One thing I will do to demonstrate love to my friends this week is... _____
_____
_____
_____

One thing I heard my friend say or do this week that indicates she understands something of what I have tried to work on this week is... _____
_____
_____
_____

One way I can say, "I love you" to my best friend this week (without using these words) is... _____
_____
_____
_____

A true friend brings out the best in us. For me this means...
_____
_____
_____

5

LOVING
THOᴙE YOU DATE

FLIRTING USED TO BE A WAY OF LIFE

and a source of excitement. Now I understand that the real fun will happen when I say, "I've waited for you." —Sarah, age 16

It used to be curiosity. Now the struggle is knowing what's there and not touching. I've learned that touching only leads to trouble. —Mark, age 16

Being physical is addictive. For me to stay pure means I must remain sexually sober. —Randy, age 14

Justin and Amy have been dating for almost six months. They plan on going to the prom together and attending the school sports banquet as a couple. They have known each other since fifth grade and have often gone to each other's homes to work on homework together. They also attend church parties together and go to each other's family get-togethers. They have become very familiar with each other's likes and dislikes.

Over the months they have been dating, they have spent a considerable amount of time holding hands, kissing, sitting next to each other on the couch, and massaging each other's shoulders and feet. After a meaningful night at a nice restaurant, Justin felt comfortable with asking Amy to become more sexual than they have ever been. When he made his suggestion, Amy…

How would you complete the story? _____

_____

_____

_____

_____

_____

_____

_____

_____

_____

How do you think Justin would respond? _____

_____

_____

_____

Regardless of how you completed the story, their lives would change forever. If they decided to become more involved physically, if someone got angry and left, or if they decided mutually to not touch each other, their lives would be different.

Males and females are wired to enjoy the presence of the opposite sex. That's what makes dating so much fun, and that's why it can be so tempting at the same time. Our minds capture and hold onto things we experience; and the imprinting that is done results in a lifetime of memories, good and bad.

Your parents have most likely told you that you should date only people you would want to marry because dating often leads to marriage. But more importantly, remember that the people you date will help you decide what kind of person you want to spend the rest of your life with and will show you what kind of person you are. You also will base much of your future love experiences on the history you create while you are a teenager—good and bad, beautiful and ugly, meaningful and devastating. The experiences you have now will influence your yet-to-come relationships.

What type of person do you want to marry? What do you want him or her to look or act like?_____
_____
_____

What do you think your future spouse will want you to be like?
_____
_____

The scary thing is that we can mess these things up so easily with some stupid choices we make as teenagers. The things we say with our mouths, see with our eyes, think in our minds, and do with our bodies can lead to a lifetime of bad memories.

That's why deciding to find good ways to love and be loved and remain sexually pure is so important. Dating can be a blast! Finding out what you want in a boyfriend or girlfriend is one of the most interesting quests you will undertake while you are a teenager.

What is so fun about spending time with the opposite sex? (Check all that apply.)

☐ Being like everybody else
☐ Having someone to do things with so I'm not alone
☐ Feeling crazy emotions
☐ Getting help with my homework
☐ Impressing my other friends
☐ Helping me know more about me
☐ Confirming my self-worth
☐ Doing the "in" thing
☐ Other: _____

One of the most incredible feelings teens can experience is the ecstasy of falling for someone. It's hard to explain—the other person just causes your mind to freeze, your heart to pound, and your emotions to spike.

Your body was put together by God for enjoyment. But you must keep the pleasure factor within proper boundaries. Holding hands for the first time causes unbelievable emotions. Hugs and kisses bring about more intense emotions. Before you know it, your body is screaming, "More!"

Your parents respond with "You'd better not do it!" The church says, "You are bad if you do it!" Many schools are saying, "Here's how to do it." Peers are saying, "I've done it." And your body is saying, "I want to do it!"

Understanding the reasons why we need to wait to have sex and learning ways to say, "I love you" appropriately can save us a lot of grief! The problem is we're not at all sure how to express our love appropriately to someone of the opposite sex.

How do you show your boy/girlfriend that you love him or her? (Check all that apply.)

☐ Hold hands
☐ Hug
☐ Kiss
☐ Talk on the phone
☐ Watch movies with explicit sexual content
☐ Touch him or her in private areas
☐ Have sex with him or her

It may seem sort of weird to see some of these things on the page, yet many students believe those things are acceptable ways to express love.

Where's the Line?

It's tough to know exactly where the line of trouble is that results in sexual temptation. Where do you think the line is?

_____
_____
_____
_____
_____

"How can a young man keep his way pure? By keeping your word" (Ps. 119:9).

Your friends may have different ideas about "the line." How do your ideas differ from those of your friends? _____

_____
_____
_____
_____
_____
_____

The Bible gives some good advice on setting the limits for sexual purity. Read I Thessalonians 4:1-8 and Galatians 5:19-23 and list guidelines (do's) and boundaries (don'ts) for relating to the opposite sex.

Do _____
_____
_____
_____
_____
_____
_____
_____
_____

Don't _____
_____
_____
_____
_____
_____
_____
_____

Now read Romans 1:26–27 and Leviticus 18:22 and add an appropriate "don't" to the list above.

These two Scriptures tell us exactly what God has to say about homosexual relationships. They warn us not to get sexually involved with someone of the same sex. Today's culture is being told that same-sexed relationships are natural and acceptable. The Bible tells us the truth: homosexuality is a sin and a perversion of sex as God created it.

What Is Sexual Purity?

So what's the big deal about staying sexually pure until you get married? Actually, remaining sexually pure should last for a lifetime. Sexual purity means more than just not having sex before you get married. It also means not telling dirty jokes; not looking at pornography on the Internet, in magazines, or on videos; not rubbing up against or touching the other person's body (other than your spouse) in sexual ways; not making obscene phone calls or using sex-lines on the telephone; and not fantasizing about being sexual with someone you aren't married to.

How can you make a commitment to sexual purity for a lifetime?

_____

_____

_____

_____

_____

_____

_____

Many churches and school groups around the world have used the True Love Waits emphasis to encourage students to protect themselves from the negative impacts of sex outside of marriage and other impure actions. If you are interested in making this commitment for the first time or making a renewal of this promise, complete the box below with this commitment.

> **"Believing that true love waits, I make a commitment to God, myself, my family, my friends, my future mate, and my future children to a lifetime of purity including sexual abstinence from this day until the day I enter a biblical marriage relationship."**
>
> **Signed** _____ **Date** _____

Look at some verses that make promises about our sexual behaviors. Match them with the correct promise.

1. Romans 6:13
2. Galatians 5:16
3. Galatians 6:9
4. 1 John 2:1

a. Jesus will be there if you fail.
b. Waiting will be worth it!
c. The cravings can go away.
d. You can honor God with your body.

God wants us to have a blast in life, and that may include dating. He promises us He will give us the wishes of our hearts. He will help us find happiness when we guard our bodies from immoral acts. He will be there if we fail. Now that doesn't give us permission to go out and mess up sexually because we know we can say, "I'm sorry" and get forgiven. It means when we get "human" and fail, He will still be God.

Becoming sexually active is easy. It does not take a college degree to mess around with inappropriate sexual behaviors. In fact, it doesn't take any thinking to have sex before you get married. When you don't think and you let your body take over, the lack of self-control can get you into trouble. Before you know it, you are breaking God's rules because it feels good, gives a temporary rush, and meets all of your selfish desires. Oddly enough, these acts say "I love me" instead of "I love you."

Say "I Love You" to Someone of the Opposite Sex

Write the name of the person you are dating or a close friend of the opposite-sex ._____

Many of you who are working through this book have never had a dating relationship. There is absolutely nothing wrong with that. In fact, if you focus on building friendships with the opposite sex instead of seeking romance, you are probably making wiser decisions than those who start dating at a young age.

In the list below, circle the actions that would most appropriately show your affection for an opposite-sex friend or a date.

 Words of Affirmation

Say, "I like your hair that way." "You give me something to look forward to during the school day." "Thank you for not laughing at me." "Thanks for laughing with me." "You make me feel great." "You make me laugh when I have been sad for too long."

 Quality Time

Talk about early childhood memories, parties, and school experiences. Do something together with friends. Go on walks.

 Gifts

Give small, inexpensive or free gifts on month anniversaries or special dates. If you normally don't pay, surprise your opposite-sex friend by treating him or her for the evening. Pick some flowers (even if they are pretty weeds) to give her. Buy him a small book that has a special message.

 Acts of Service

Ask his or her parents if you could help with a specific household chore or job and don't expect any payment. Make a meal for him or her instead of going to a restaurant. Offer to put up your supper dishes after a meal at his or her parents' home. Offer to help around the house while you are waiting for her to get ready.

 Physical Touch

Hold hands. Hug. Rub each other's feet. Lean on each other while watching television or a movie. Offer a neck or shoulder rub. Sit close.

How Can I Do This?

The good news about these five ways to say "I love you" is that you will stay safe and not have to worry about any negative consequences and bad memories.

Understanding how to speak words of affirmation helps you to stay away from such phrases as "I want...," "You owe me...," or "I deserve...." Saying supportive words will affirm your genuine love.

What are some words of appreciation, encouragement, and respect that your date needs to hear from you? _____
_____
_____
_____
_____

Using appropriate physical touch indicates how much you truly love the other person. Touching someone in places that are off-limits results in devaluing the other person and makes the person nothing more than an object to you.

How could misusing physical touch impact both lives in a relationship? _____
_____
_____
_____
_____

Spending quality time talking and listening to each other replaces the temptation to be consumed with passion. But be cautious of sexual temptation that can develop when you spend long periods of time together in secluded places.

What are some limits you need to set on times and places you are alone with your date?

_____

_____

_____

_____

_____

_____

_____

_____

_____

_____

_____

_____

_____

_____

_____

Instead of giving your body away, consider the value of offering gifts that have nothing to do with your sexuality. You'll be glad you waited someday! We can't help but compare one thing to another. If we have to take this "law of comparison" to bed with us, we may miss out on fully enjoying the person that we want to spend the rest of our life with. Sexual abstinence now will help you avoid future comparisons with past partners.

Demonstrate your love by acts of service instead of sexual acts. Invest your time wisely in doing acts of kindness for your date, his or her family, and other people. Sexually acting out is purely selfish, whereas meeting the needs of others is totally awesome.

Learning to express yourself not only impacts the way you show love but also helps you set boundaries for sexual purity and happiness.

Weekly Observations

Many television shows and movies focus on dating relationships. Some are healthy and some are not. List the shows
that you know about that depict boyfriends and girlfriends
interacting._____

_____
_____
_____
_____

What are the good qualities displayed by these relationships?

_____
_____

What one thing about these relationships do you not want to
model with your dates? _____

_____

What songs did you hear this week that discussed the
relationships between persons of the opposite sex? What
acts of service, gifts, words of affirmation, quality time, and
physical touch were mentioned? _____

_____
_____

While spending time with your boy/girlfriend or any
friend of the opposite sex this week, what did you hear the
person say he or she needed in order to feel loved by you or
other friends? _____

_____
_____

Take a look at the e-mail list you made on page 9. If you have access to a computer, write to your boy/girlfriend or a person of the opposite sex and tell the person one limit or boundary you need to set in your relationship because of how much you appreciate him or her for who he or she is and what he or she means to you.

Prayer

Ask God to help you be a perfect example of the way a teenager should love in a dating relationship. Ask God to help you overcome some of your temptations. Be specific about your requests and needs. Pray that God would prepare you for the person you will eventually marry and pray for the other person (even though you don't know who he or she is yet) as he or she stays pure for your future relationship.

"No one should despise your youth; instead you should be an example to believers in speech, in conduct, in love, in faith, in purity" (1 Tim. 4:12).

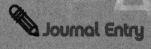 **Journal Entry**

Date _____

Some of the things I will do this week to show my love to a friend of the opposite sex are...

_____
_____
_____
_____
_____
_____
_____
_____
_____

One thing I need to stop doing this week with my boy/girl-friend is... (If you are embarrassed to write it down or are afraid that someone will find this journal page, write down a letter or word that would remind you of your answer but would mean nothing to anybody else.) _____

_____
_____
_____
_____

One thing I will do this week to stay sexually pure is... _____

_____
_____

One way I can say, "I love you" to a person of the opposite sex (without using these words) this week is... _____

_____
_____

Love means waiting until the right time and the best way to express it. For me this means... _____

_____

_____

_____

_____

_____

_____

SESSION 1
Looking for Love

Overview
In this session students will learn to define real love.

Before the Session
- **For Step 1:** Hide and display around the room a variety of objects, words, or pictures that depict love from family, friends, and dating relationships. Write *Looking for Love* on a poster and display it on a wall near a table. Provide markers nearby.
- **For Step 2:** Obtain enough *TLW: A Student's Guide to the Five Love Languages* books to provide one for each participant.
- **For Step 3:** Provide pencils for each participant.
- **For Step 6:** Obtain enough note cards to give each student three.

Step 1
As students arrive, ask them to search the room for objects that suggest what people might look for when they are trying to find love. Direct students to place the objects on a focal table. Invite them to write on the poster where people are looking for love.

Step 2
After everyone has arrived, say, **Today's teenagers are bombarded with mixed messages concerning love. For the next four weeks we are going to look for better ways to say, "I love you" to family members, friends, and those we date.** Lead teenagers to discuss how the items they found represent love. Ask, **What are the various relationships we participate in?** Ask volunteers to share their answers from the *Looking for Love* poster.

Distribute the books and review the format of the chapters with the students. Point out the bold-faced response activities throughout each chapter, the "Weekly Observations" guidelines for doing activities during the week, and the "Journal Entry" page for recording thoughts and feelings throughout the week. Explain that they will need to complete these activities to prepare for the session each week. The assignments will ask them to do such things as listen to music, watch television shows or movies, and interact with others.

Ask students to work through Chapters 1 and 2 to prepare for next week. Encourage them to find a time when they can work on the book daily. Call attention to the Five Love Languages Profile on pages 27-28. Urge them to complete the profile so they can participate in the discussion next week.

Step 3

Ask students to look on page 11 at the four Scripture verses that describe how people in the Bible tried to substitute sexual fulfillment for love. Give them time to look up these verses and match them to the bad sexual choices made. (Answers: 1–d, 2–a, 3–c, 4–b) Ask for brief comments on the four sexual relationships.

Lead students to briefly discuss how people can experience real love in their relationships with friends and why that may not happen. Lead them to discuss how people can experience love from their family and obstacles to that source of love. Ask, **How do some people use things to try to fill their need for love?**

Step 4

Lead students to read "So What Is Love?" on pages 14-15. Discuss the questions in that section.

Step 5

Work through "What's the Point?" on pages 15-17. Ask students to place a check mark in the boxes on page 15, if they haven't already done so, and discuss what they checked. Read aloud the final paragraph on page 15. Ask a volunteer to read 1 Corinthians 13:4-7 aloud and then ask students to name ways of showing love found in the passage. Ask another volunteer to read aloud Romans 12:9-21 and then ask students to share their advice letters on page 16. If students have not written letters, ask them to get into small groups, to decide on a question that a teen may ask about inappropriate expressions of love, and to write a response to that question. Ask groups to share their letters.

Step 6
Say, **One of the ways we share love with others is through words of affirmation.** Ask students to discuss words of affirmation that mean the most to them.

Give each student three note cards. Direct them to write brief notes of encouragement to three persons in the group: the person they know best, the person they know least, and someone they look up to. After students have completed their cards, gather them up, redistribute them to the appropriate persons, and close the session in prayer.

SESSION 2
Understanding Love Languages

Overview
In this session students will discuss their primary love languages.

Before the Session
- **For Step 1:** Obtain from a local library "learn to speak" tapes of two foreign languages. Set up two tape players and play these tapes as students arrive. On a tear sheet, write the word LOVE as an acrostic down the left side. Display it on a wall and provide markers nearby.
- **For Step 2:** Bring three CDs of different styles of music and set

up CD players in separate areas of the room.
- **For Step 3:** Provide paper and pencils.
- **For Step 4:** Print each love language on a separate note card and display as you discuss them. Place them on the LOVE banner.

Step 1

As students enter, check to make sure they have completed the profile on pages 27-28 in their book. Ask those who haven't to go somewhere they can have privacy and complete the profile as the group is going through this first activity.

Instruct teenagers to write on the LOVE acrostic banner different ways we say "I love you" that start with these letters. Once everyone has arrived, say, **Love can be spoken in many languages and in many ways.** Review some of the words and phrases from the LOVE acrostic.

Step 2

Ask students to form three groups and send each group to one of the CD players. Say, **As you listen to music you can hear a variety of ways love is expressed.** Ask groups to listen to the provided CD for five minutes and list different ways love is expressed. When time is up, ask the groups to share their lists with the large group.

Step 3

Comment on the number of answers from the listening groups that have to do with giving. Say, **Jesus showed us love when He gave up His life to provide forgiveness for our sins.** Direct attention to page 32 for other ways that Jesus showed love. Ask various youth to look up and read the passages listed and then share their answers. *(Answers: 1–d, 2–c, 3–e, 4–a, 5–b)* Ask, **In what ways has Jesus shown His love for you personally?** After responses, give each student paper and a pencil. Ask students to write a thank-you note to Jesus.

Step 4
Briefly discuss the five love languages using the list on page 30 and the chart on page 32. Ask students to find page 29 in their workbook and share what their main love language is. Once everyone has shared their love language, ask youth to sit in a group with others who have the same main love language.

Ask the groups to discuss how their family and friends have most effectively met their need for love. Allow time for discussion; then ask the groups to take turns sharing responses with the large group. Suggest students note good ideas on page 34 under the appropriate love language.

Step 5
Call the groups back into the large group. Lead the students to discuss how giving could affect a teenager's sexual purity and decision to remain sexually abstinent. Ask, **What are some things you could give that would say, "I love you" to the person you date or like?**

Pair up participants in male/female dyads. Put remaining youth in one group. Have students discuss what sexual purity means and share how they can stay pure from the inside out.

Step 6
Ask students to find a partner. Instruct them to take a five-minute walk or sit and talk. Encourage them to listen carefully to each other. Emphasize the importance of focused attention in showing love. Tell them to pray together after their walk. Then, either dismiss them or bring them back together for the following comments.

Say, **Discovering our main love language is important in building relationships. Learning to give and take will help all relationships become more significant.** Conclude the session by praying that God would give students opportunities to love appropriately in many different ways.

SESSION 3
Loving Your Family

Overview
In this session students will learn how to demonstrate love to their parents and siblings.

Before the Session
- **For Step 1:** Make name tags labeled *father, mother, daughter,* or *son*. Provide one for each group member.
- **For Step 4:** Create signs naming the five love languages, one language per sign, and post them in different parts of the room. Make sure each sign allows room for response and place markers near each.
- **For Step 6:** Provide a note card for each student.

Step 1
As students arrive assign them the role of father, mother, daughter, or son by giving them the appropriate name tag. Divide students into families of three or four. Remember all families are not traditional and may not have one of each character. If there is a group of two left, let them be a family. If there is a youth left alone, place him or her with another group. Ask each "family" to read the three scenarios on page 39 and choose one of the situations to act out. Ask each group to perform their role play for the large group, and allow the students to guess which family the performers are acting like.

Step 2
Comment, **Every day we encounter families that are different from ours. How are the role-play families like the people you interact with each day? What problems do you see with these families we just portrayed?**

Step 3

Ask students to turn to page 41. Allow time for students to fill in the blanks if they have not already done so. Then lead students to discuss: **What insight did you gain from this activity?**

Ask youth to voice sentence prayers that begin "Thank you, God, for my dad/mom who shows his/her love by...." Close the prayer by thanking God for parents who love their children.

Step 4

Direct students to page 46 and lead them to write the name of each member of their family and the person's love language, if they have not already done this.

Call attention to the signs posted around the room. Explain that when you say "go," the students are to go to a sign that tells one family member's love language. They are to then write on the poster something they have done for that family member to make him or her feel loved. Allow three minutes work time; then say "go" again to signal students to move to another sign that tells another family member's love language. Repeat several times; then ask the students to sit.

Ask, **Which love language is hardest for you to "speak"?** Lead students to review the responses on the different posters and then write one thing they will do to show love to each family member.

Step 5

Instruct all students to look at pages 44-45 in this book. Ask students to form small groups with others who have the same role on their name tags from step 1. Say, **Take a few minutes to look up and read Proverbs 7, fill in the blanks, and discuss the questions.**

Then ask the large group, **What are some words of advice you have been given by your parents? Which words of advice have helped? Which words of advice have seemed off-base to you? Has anyone followed advice that seemed stupid and discovered it worked better than expected?**

Step 6

Ask each student to write his or her name on a note card. Pick the cards up and redistribute them. Ensure that no one gets his own card. Ask students not to tell whose name they got. Explain that the assignment this week is to give a gift to the person whose card they got. Share the rules: (1) they cannot spend anything to get the gift; (2) the gift has to have meaning to them; (3) it has to have meaning for the person they give it to. If students need help, explain that they might give something they already have or something they make out of materials they already have. If a member of the group is not present, ask another student to also bring a gift for that student, or make or bring that student a gift yourself. Close in prayer.

SESSION 4
Loving Your Friends

Overview
In this session students will discuss ways to express love to friends.

Before the Session
• **For Step 1:** Collect newspaper pages that contain television listings to be used as posters. Display them on a focal wall and place markers nearby. Provide snacks and background music to create a more social atmosphere.
• **For Step 2:** Provide tear sheets and markers.

Step 1
As students arrive, call attention to the newspaper pages and ask them to list television shows that feature friendships. These may be current shows or ones from years ago. Invite them to help themselves to some snacks and to tell each other some of the funniest experiences they've had with good friends.

Step 2

Divide the class into two groups. Ask each group to look at the lists of television shows and add others to them. Ask one group to list good qualities displayed in the television friendships. Ask the other group to list negative qualities displayed in the television friendships. Combine the groups when they are finished and ask students to share their responses. Encourage the students to read between the lines of some of the relationships for added characteristics.

Step 3

Ask the students to form groups according to their gender. Ask the girls to look up Ruth 1:3-18 and the guys to look up 1 Samuel 18:1-3; 19:1-7. Instruct them to read their passage and then answer the questions on page 55. Ask them to discuss the importance of same-gender friendships. When finished, ask the groups to share their responses with each other.

Step 4

Say, **Friends express their affection in a variety of ways. The most common way is spending quality time together.**

Instruct the students to turn to page 60. Ask different students to read the Bible passages. After each passage is read, ask students to identify the friends in the passage and choose which love language is shown. (*Answers: 1–Joseph and the king of Egypt, c; 2–Ruth and Naomi, a; 3–Jonathan and David, c; 4–Elijah and Elisha, d; 5–the twelve apostles and the seven deacons, e; 6–Aquila, Priscilla, and Paul, b; 7–Paul and Timothy, d; 8–Paul and the Philippian church members, a*)

Step 5

Instruct students to turn to page 62. If they haven't had a chance to fill in the names of their friends and their main love languages, allow a few minutes for them to do so. If they have friends in the group, allow them to ask those friends what their main love language is.

After students have had a chance to review the suggestions on page 63, ask volunteers to name what their own main love language is and then share something a friend has done for them that really meant a lot to them. Try to get a volunteer for each love language to share. Share from your own life if necessary. Suggest students write the good ideas on page 62 to help them show affection to their friends in a way they will most appreciate.

Step 6
Ask, **How can friends impact an individual's sexual purity? In what ways can you influence friends to treat their bodies and the bodies of the persons they date like they are God's temples? How can friends help with the question, "How far is too far?"**
Invite each person to pair up with another student and each share one concern that they need to be held accountable for. (*Examples: setting limits on dates, respecting their parents, getting rid of some pornography, staying off certain Internet sites*) Invite the pairs to pray for each other and then lead the entire group in a closing prayer thanking God for friends, quality time with them and Him, and for the courage to live a purer life during the next week.
Wrap up the session by telling the students to give 10 holy hugs to their friends before they leave. If your group isn't accustomed to hugs, suggest they give hugs or handshakes.

SESSION 5
Loving Those You Date

Overview
Students will learn to express pure love to the opposite sex.

Before the Session
• **For Step 1:** Prepare a banner by writing the words *CROSSING THE LINE!* on a tear sheet. Provide markers nearby. Obtain at least

two VCR or DVD players and set them up to play scenes depicting opposite-sex relationships.

• **For Step 2:** Provide video cameras for groups of four to use for "man-on-the-street" interviews. Prepare questionnaires for the interviews, including these questions: "How old should you be before you start dating?", "When was your first kiss?", "What are some good limits to set on dates?", and "What word of advice would you give to dating high school couples?"

• **For Step 3:** Provide tear sheets and markers.

Step 1

As students arrive, suggest they watch the scenes showing opposite-sex relationships. Instruct them to write on the CROSSING THE LINE! banner positive and negative examples in the scenes.

Step 2

Form teams of four. Tell students that their assignment is to go out and get on-the-street interviews using the video camera and questions they will be given. Say, **You don't have much time, so work as quickly as you can.** Give each team a video camera and a questionnaire. Specify a time for students to return.

Step 3

Play the student videotapes and list the recommended physical and sexual boundaries. Ask for comments from the students. Ask students to get with a partner to work through "What Is Sexual Purity?" on pages 74-75 (or review it if they've already done it). Review answers to the matching exercise on page 75. *(Answers: 1–d, 2–c, 3–b, 4–a)* Say, **Sexual purity means more than not having intercourse before marriage. What else does it mean?**

Step 4

Ask students to turn to page 73. Ask a volunteer to read aloud 1 Thessalonians 4:1-8 as other students follow along in their Bibles. Lead the group to name guidelines given in this passage (do's) and boundaries (don'ts). Instruct students to list the responses on page 73. Then repeat the process for Galatians 5:19-23; Romans 1:26-27; and Leviticus 18:22.

Say, **Many of you in this study have never had a dating relationship. There is absolutely nothing wrong with that. In fact, if you focus on building friendships with those of the opposite sex instead of seeking romance, you are probably making wiser decisions than those who start dating at a young age.**

Step 5

Instruct students to turn to pages 77-78 and discuss ways to use the five love languages as suggestions for sexual purity. Some of the students will be ready to make a commitment to sexual purity after this study. Encourage each student to look at the True Love Waits Commitment on page 74 and consider signing it. If they have signed one before this will serve as a recommitment. If they have never signed one and they want to today, ask them to share their decision with a youth worker and their parents.

Read Psalm 119:9 and ask students to name other ways that have been discussed during this study to maintain sexual purity.

Step 6

Encourage students to choose a friend in the group and determine one act of service they could do for that friend that would show genuine love.

Pray that God would help these students fill their lives with the five expressions of love instead of impure sexual thoughts and actions.

CHRISTIAN GROWTH STUDY PLAN

Preparing Christians to Serve

In the **Christian Growth Study Plan (formerly Church Study Course),** this book *True Love Waits: A Student's Guide to the Five Love Languages* is a resource for course credit in the subject area Personal Life of the Christian Growth category of plans. To receive credit, read the book, complete the learning activities, show your work to your pastor, a staff member or church leader, then complete the following information. This page may be duplicated. Send the completed page to:

Christian Growth Study Plan
One LifeWay Plaza
Nashville, TN 37234-0117
FAX: (615)251-5067
Email: cgspnet@lifeway.com
For information about the Christian Growth Study Plan, refer to the Christian Growth Study Plan Catalog. It is located online at www.lifeway.com/cgsp. If you do not have access to the Internet, contact the Christian Growth Study Plan office (1.800.968.5519) for the specific plan you need for your ministry.

True Love Waits: A Student's Guide to the Five Love Languages
COURSE NUMBER: CG-0994

PARTICIPANT INFORMATION

Social Security Number (USA ONLY-optional)	Personal CGSP Number*	Date of Birth (MONTH, DAY, YEAR)
– –	–	– –

Name (First, Middle, Last)	Home Phone
	– –

Address (Street, Route, or P.O. Box)	City, State, or Province	Zip/Postal Code

Please check appropriate box: ❑ Resource purchased by self ❑ Resource purchased by church ❑ Other

CHURCH INFORMATION

Church Name

Address (Street, Route, or P.O. Box)	City, State, or Province	Zip/Postal Code

CHANGE REQUEST ONLY

☐ Former Name

☐ Former Address	City, State, or Province	Zip/Postal Code

☐ Former Church	City, State, or Province	Zip/Postal Code

Signature of Pastor, Conference Leader, or Other Church Leader	Date

*New participants are requested but not required to give SS# and date of birth. Existing participants, please give CGSP# when using SS# for the first time. Thereafter, only one ID# is required. **Mail to:** Christian Growth Study Plan, One LifeWay Plaza, Nashville, TN 37234-0117. Fax: (615)251-5067.

Rev. 3-03

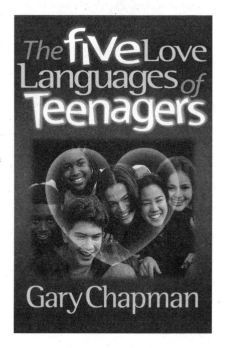